# Dear *Dad*
## from you to me®

JOURNALS®
of a LIFETIME
made with love *from you to me*

# Dear Dad
## from you to me®

This book is for your Father's unique and amazing story.

It is for him to capture some of his life's key memories, experiences and feelings.

Ask him to complete it carefully and, if he wants to, add some photographs or images to personalise it more.

When it is finished and returned to you, this will be a record of his story . . . a story that you will treasure forever.

*Dear*

*Here is a gift from me to you . . . for you to give to me.*

*When we are children we are always asking questions
. . . well I now have some more for you.*

*Please could you answer them in the way that only you know
how and then give the book back to me.*

*There might be a couple of questions that you prefer not to
answer, so don't worry, just answer the others as well as you
can . . . I won't mind.*

*People say that we all have at least one book in us, and this
will be one of yours.*

*The story of you and me that I will treasure forever.*

*Thank you,*

*with love*

Tell me about the time and place you were born . . .

What are your earliest memories?

# Tell me about your Mum and Dad ...

What do you think your parents thought of you as a child?

What interesting information do you know
about other people in our family?

Please detail what you know of our family tree . . .

Here's some space for you to add more about our family that will interest generations to come . . .

What do you remember about the place/s you lived when you were a child?

What were your favourite childhood toys or games?

Tell me about your **best friend/s** as a young child . . .

What do you remember about your holidays as a child?

What sort of pets did you have when you were young and what were their names?

What were you best at when you were at school?

What did you want to do when you grew up?

Who was your best friend as a teenager . . .
and why?

What were your favourite hobbies when you were young?

Did you have an idol when you were young?
Tell me who and why . . .

What was the first piece of music you bought?

What piece/s of music would you choose in your own favourite 'top 10' from when you were young?

Describe any family traditions you had
or maybe still have . . .

What age were you when you started work?
Tell me about the jobs you have had . . .

What was the first car you owned?

Tell me about the other vehicles you have had . . .

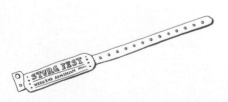

# How did you meet my Mother?

What would you do for a night-out when you were dating?

Tell me about a memorable piece of music that you and Mum had 'just for you' . . .

Describe a special day you had with my Mother . . .

How did you feel when you found out you were going to be a father?

What did you think when you first saw me after I was born?

What were my **statistics** when I was ${\rm born}$ ...
time of birth, weight, height etc?

What did I look like when I was born?

If you have a photo, could you stick it here please . . .

What was my **nickname** before I was born or when I was young?

Before I was born, what other names had you thought of calling me?

What was the first word or words you remember me saying?

Describe some of the favourite memories you have of me when I was a child . . .

What was I like when I was a child?

What attributes did I have as a child that I still have now?

What were you most proud of about me when I was at school?

Describe what you like about me . . .

Is there anything you would like to change
about me?

What are the happiest or greatest memories
of your life?

What are a few of your favourite things?

Tell me about the things that make you laugh . . .

Describe your memory of some major world events that have happened in your lifetime . . .

Describe the greatest change that you have seen in your lifetime so far . . .

Describe something you still want to achieve in your life . . .

Tell me about the dreams you have for your life . . .

If you were an animal . . . what type of animal would you be, and why?

If you won the Lottery . . . what would you do with the money?

What have you found most difficult in your life?

What is your **biggest regret** in your life?

Can you do anything about it **now?**

With hindsight what would you do differently?

Tell me something you think I won't know about you . . .

How do you like to be thought of by others?

Is there anything you would like to say sorry for?

What piece of **advice** would you like to **offer** me?

And now your chance to write anything else you want to say to me . . .

These extra pages are for us to write any
**questions, memories** or **answers** that
may not have been covered elsewhere in the book . . .

*And finally for the record . . .*


what is your full name ?


what is your date of birth ?


what colour are your eyes ?


how tall are you ?


what blood group are you ?


what was the date when you completed this story for me ?

*And a few words to thank you for*
*completing this Journal of a Lifetime ...*

Published by **FROM YOU TO ME**

For a full range of all our titles where journals
& books can also be personalised, please visit

**WWW.FROMYOUTOME.COM**

# Dear Dad
### from you to me®

Sketch collection first published by **JOURNALS OF A LIFETIME**, an imprint of **FROM YOU TO ME LTD**, in January 2012.

9   11   13   15   14   12   10

Copyright, from you to me limited 2007

ISBN 978–1–907048–45–6

Designed and published in the UK.

Printed and bound in China by Imago. This paper is manufactured from pulp sourced from forests that are legally and sustainably managed.

For permission requests, contact the publisher at their head office address:

**FROM YOU TO ME**
Waterhouse
Waterhouse Lane
Monkton Combe
Bath, BA2 7JA, UK

HELLO@FROMYOUTOME.COM
WWW.FROMYOUTOME.COM